B.C.—RIGHT ON

by Johnny Hart

A FAWCETT GOLD MEDAL BOOK

Fawcett Publications, Inc., Greenwich, Conn.

Fawcett Gold Medal Books by Johnny Hart:

B.C. ON THE ROCKS   D2510

HEY! B.C. (abridged)   D2229

TAKE A BOW, B.C.   D2215

B.C. IS ALIVE AND WELL   D2117

B.C. STRIKES BACK (abridged)   D2091

50¢ Wherever Paperbacks Are Sold

If your bookdealer is sold out, send cover price plus 15¢ for
postage and handling to Mail Order Service, Fawcett Publi
cations, Inc., Greenwich, Conn. Please order by number and
title. Orders accepted only for United States and Posses
sions. A free catalog of Fawcett Crest, Gold Medal, and
Premier Books is available upon request.

5.2

hart

5.4

5·5

5-6

5-8

hart

5-11

5·18

5-20

hart

5·22

hart.

5-23

hart.

5·25

5-26

hart.

pōl·lu'tion *n.*
the result of
polluting.

pōl·lu'ting.
to pollute.

pōl·lute'.
to cause
pollution

5·29

5·30

5-31

6·1

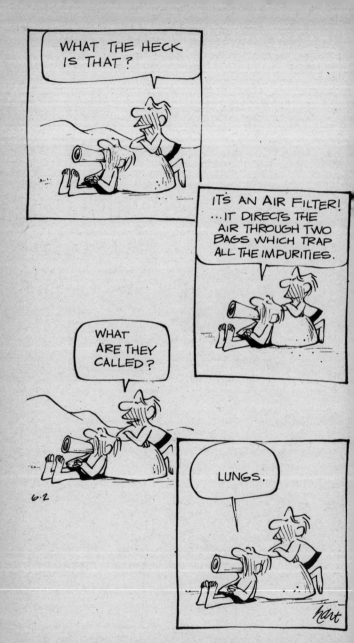

6·5

6·6

6·7

68

hart

6·13

614

6-15

RING

RING

6-19

HELLO....

hart

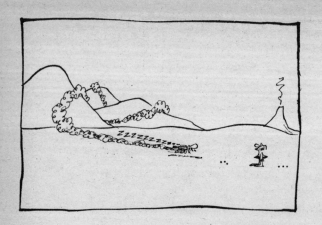

BEEP BEEP!

6·21

....SNEAKERS?

hart

6.24

6·26

6·27

6·28

6·29

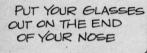

PUT YOUR GLASSES
OUT ON THE END
OF YOUR NOSE

4·30

YOUR TOENAILS
COULD USE CUTTING.

hart

7·1

SLAM

RING

7-3

hart

7-4

HONK

hart

7.7

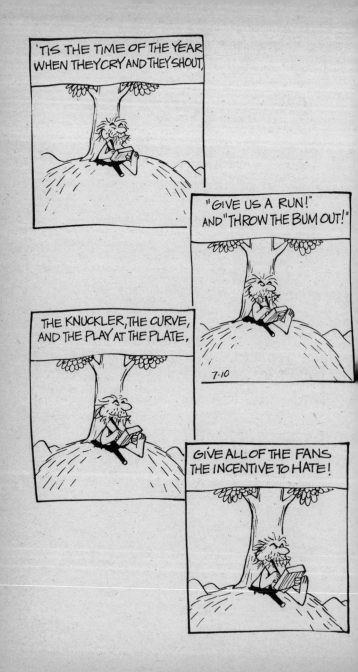

7-11

POOK

7-12

YOU JUST 'SHOOK-OFF'
EVERY PITCH YOU'VE GOT!
WHAT THE HECK DO YOU
WANT TO DO?

7-13

BEAN THE UMPIRE.

hart

7.14

hart

TIME! ...LET'S TAKE A LOOK AT THAT BALL!

7:15

COME ON, NOW! ..IT CAN'T BE THAT BIG!

hart

7-24

7·25

SPROING

ZAK

7-27

I WASN'T GONNA EAT IT!
I WAS JUST GONNA SMELL IT!

hart.

1

7-28

SMACK

7·29

nart

8·9

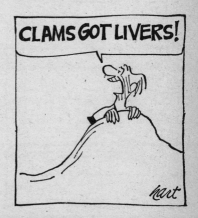

8·11

AN APPLE FOR
YOUR THOUGHTS!

8·14

WILL YOU GET
OUT OF HERE!

hart

8-18

hart

HI, THERE, PUSSY CAT, ...
I AM A PELICAN, ...
MY BEAK CAN HOLD MORE THAN
MY BELLY CAN.

8-21

I THINK I'M IN
LOVE WITH A POET

hart

8·22

8-23

hart

8-25

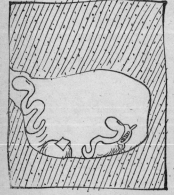

9·2

9-7

hart

9·11

9·14

9.18

9.19

9·20

9.22

9.26

CLAP

AAAAAAAHHHHH

10·3

hart

10.6

CRACK **NAB**
SWISH **TAG**
SWISH
NAB **TAG**

TRIPLE PLAY!

10-7

10·11

10·16

1019

10-21

10·23

hart

HI THERE, I AM AN APTERYX. A WINGLESS BIRD WITH HAIRY FEATHERS.

10-24

THERE'S SO MUCH TO LEARN......

hart

10·25

hart